Everyday Mathematics®

The University of Chicago School Mathematics Project

Math Journal Answer Book
Volume 2

Grade **1**

McGraw Hill **Wright Group**

The **McGraw·Hill** Companies

The University of Chicago School Mathematics Project (UCSMP)

Max Bell, Director, UCSMP Elementary Materials Component; Director, *Everyday Mathematics* First Edition
James McBride, Director, *Everyday Mathematics* Second Edition
Andy Isaacs, Director, *Everyday Mathematics* Third Edition
Amy Dillard, Associate Director, *Everyday Mathematics* Third Edition

Authors

Max Bell
Jean Bell
John Bretzlauf
Amy Dillard

Robert Hartfield
Andy Isaacs
James McBride
Rachel Malpass McCall*

Kathleen Pitvorec
Peter Saecker

*Third Edition only

Technical Art
Diana Barrie

Teachers in Residence
Jeanine O'Nan Brownell
Andrea Cocke
Brooke A. North

Editorial Assistant
Rossita Fernando

Contributors
Robert Balfanz, Judith Busse, Mary Ellen Dairyko, Lynn Evans, James Flanders, Dorothy Freedman, Nancy Guile Goodsell, Pam Guastafeste, Nancy Hanvey, Murray Hozinsky, Deborah Arron Leslie, Sue Lindsley, Mariana Mardrus, Carol Montag, Elizabeth Moore, Kate Morrison, William D. Pattison, Joan Pederson, Brenda Penix, June Ploen, Herb Price, Dannette Riehle, Ellen Ryan, Marie Schilling, Susan Sherrill, Patricia Smith, Robert Strang, Jaronda Strong, Kevin Sweeney, Sally Vongsathorn, Esther Weiss, Francine Williams, Michael Wilson, Izaak Wirzup

Photo Credits
©Ralph A. Clevenger/CORBIS, cover, *center;* Getty Images, cover, *bottom left;* ©Tom and Dee Ann McCarthy/CORBIS, cover *right.*

www.WrightGroup.com

Wright Group

Send all inquiries to:
Wright Group/McGraw-Hill
P.O. Box 812960
Chicago, IL 60681

ISBN-13 978-0-07-611042-1
ISBN-10 0-07-611042-7

1 2 3 4 5 6 7 8 9 CPS 12 11 10 09 08 07 06

Contents

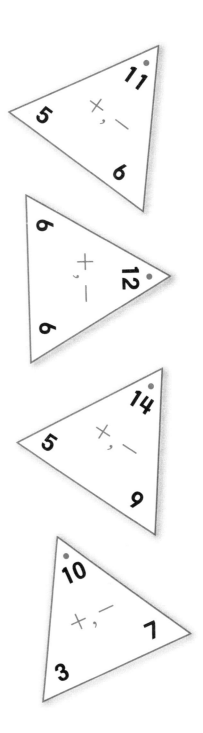

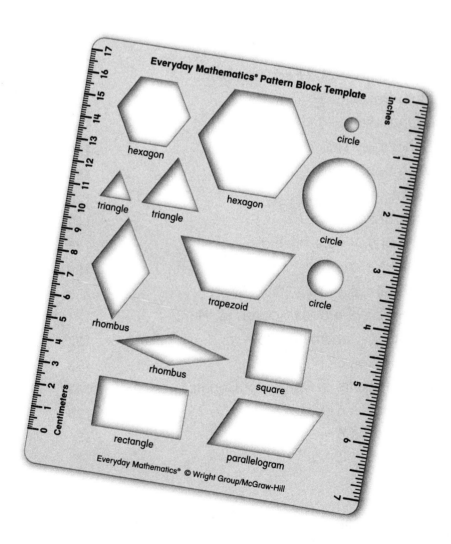

UNIT 8 Mental Arithmetic, Money, and Fractions

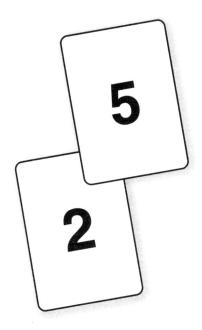

UNIT 9   Place Value and Fractions

Activity Sheets*

*Activity Sheets do not appear in the *Math Journal Answer Book.*

LESSON 6·1 Dice-Throw Record 2

Unit
dice dots

Record each fact and its turn-around fact once.

Order will vary.

												6+6	
										6+5	6+6		
								5+5	6+6	5+6			
							6+5	5+5	6+4				
						6+2	6+6	5+5	4+6				
					1+6	6+6	5+3	4+5					
					6+1	2+6	3+6	6+3					
					4+2	4+5	1+4	4+4					
					2+2	5+2	5+2	3+5					
					3+2	1+5	5+5	3+3					
					2+2	3+1	1+4	4+1					
						2+1	3+4	1+3					
						1+1	2+1						
							1+1						
							2	3	4	5	6	7	8	9	10	11	12

LESSON 6·1

Math Boxes

1. Write the sums.

$2 + 4 =$ ___6___

___5___ $= 3 + 2$

___6___ $= 1 + 5$

$4 + 0 =$ ___4___

2. What is the missing rule?

in ↓

Rule

out ↓

in	out
3	5
17	19
14	16

Fill in the circle next to the best answer.

Ⓐ +3 ●Ⓑ +2

Ⓒ −2 Ⓓ −5

3. Add.

$3 + 4 =$ ___7___

$4 + 3 =$ ___7___

$2 + 7 =$ ___9___

$7 + 2 =$ ___9___

4. Draw lines to match the shapes that look alike.

Column A   Column B

LESSON 6·2 **Name-Collection Boxes**

1. Write other names for 11.

11

8 + 3

Answers vary.

13 − 2

2. Write other names for 12.

12

1 dozen

Answers vary.

卌 卌 //

3 + 3 + 3 + 3

15 − 3

3. Cross out the names that don't belong in the 10-box.

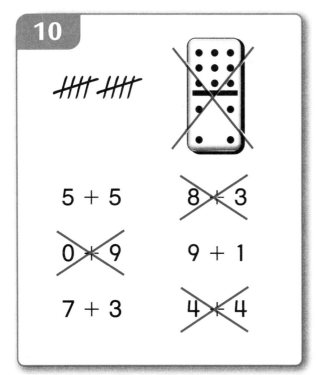

10

卌 卌

5 + 5   ~~8 + 3~~

~~0 + 9~~   9 + 1

7 + 3   ~~4 + 4~~

4. Make your own.

Answers vary.

LESSON 6·2 Math Boxes

1. Write 5 more names for 10.

> **10**
>
> 5 + 5
>
> ten
>
> ~~HHT~~ ~~HHT~~
>
> Sample answers:
> 20 − 10, 7 + 3,
> 18 − 8, diez,
> 1 + 9

2. Solve the riddles.

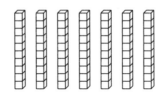

What am I? ___70___

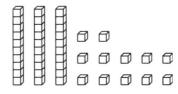

What am I? ___42___

3. Add.

2 + 2 = ___4___

3 + 3 = ___6___

4 + 4 = ___8___

5 + 5 = ___10___

4. Shade the biggest triangle.

LESSON 6·3 **Fact Families**

Write the 3 numbers for each domino.
Use the numbers to write the fact family.

1.

Numbers: __3__, __5__, __8__

Fact Family: __3__ + __5__ = __8__

__5__ + __3__ = __8__

__8__ − __5__ = __3__

__8__ − __3__ = __5__

2.

Numbers: __4__, __6__, __10__

Fact Family: __4__ + __6__ = __10__

__6__ + __4__ = __10__

__10__ − __4__ = __6__

__10__ − __6__ = __4__

3.

Numbers: __9__, __3__, __12__

Fact Family: __9__ + __3__ = __12__

__3__ + __9__ = __12__

__12__ − __3__ = __9__

__12__ − __9__ = __3__

4. Make up your own.
Draw the dots.

Numbers: __Answers vary.__, ___, ___

Fact Family: ___ + ___ = ___

___ + ___ = ___

___ − ___ = ___

___ − ___ = ___

LESSON 6·3 Name-Collection Boxes

Write as many names as you can for each number.

1.

> **13**
>
> Answers vary.
> Sample answers:
> $10 + 3$ $5 + 5 + 3$
> ~~HHT~~ ~~HHT~~ ///
> $14 - 1$ $6 + 7$

2.

> **20**
>
> Answers vary.
> Sample answers:
> $10 + 10$ $25 - 5$
> ~~HHT~~ ~~HHT~~ ~~HHT~~ ~~HHT~~
> veinte
> $5 + 5 + 5 + 5$

3. Cross out the names that don't belong in the 25 box.

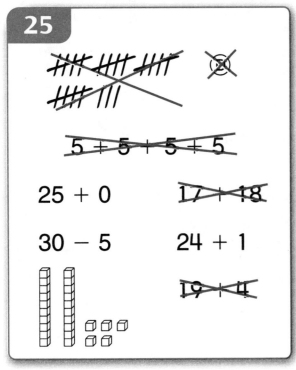

4. Choose a number. Show as many names for it as you can.

> Answers vary.

LESSON 6·3 **Math Boxes**

---

1. Write the sums.

$1 + 8 =$ ___9___

___8___ $= 6 + 2$

$$\begin{array}{r} 4 \\ + 2 \\ \hline 6 \end{array} \qquad \begin{array}{r} 7 \\ + 0 \\ \hline 7 \end{array}$$

---

2. Fill in the missing numbers.

in →

Rule

$+10$

out ↓

in	out
13	23
18	28
79	89
93	103
125	135

---

3. Add.

$5 + 4 =$ ___9___

$4 + 5 =$ ___9___

$2 + 3 =$ ___5___

$3 + 2 =$ ___5___

---

4. Draw lines to match the shapes that look alike.

Column A   Column B

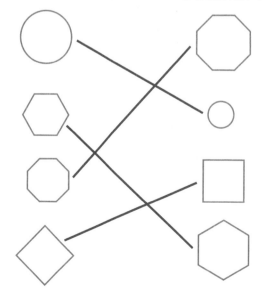

LESSON 6·4 Fact Power Table

0 + 0 0	0 + 1 1	0 + 2 2	0 + 3 3	0 + 4 4	0 + 5 5	0 + 6 6	0 + 7 7	0 + 8 8	0 + 9 9
1 + 0 1	1 + 1 2	1 + 2 3	1 + 3 4	1 + 4 5	1 + 5 6	1 + 6 7	1 + 7 8	1 + 8 9	1 + 9 10
2 + 0 2	2 + 1 3	2 + 2 4	2 + 3 5	2 + 4 6	2 + 5 7	2 + 6 8	2 + 7 9	2 + 8 10	2 + 9 11
3 + 0 3	3 + 1 4	3 + 2 5	3 + 3 6	3 + 4 7	3 + 5 8	3 + 6 9	3 + 7 10	3 + 8 11	3 + 9 12
4 + 0 4	4 + 1 5	4 + 2 6	4 + 3 7	4 + 4 8	4 + 5 9	4 + 6 10	4 + 7 11	4 + 8 12	4 + 9 13
5 + 0 5	5 + 1 6	5 + 2 7	5 + 3 8	5 + 4 9	5 + 5 10	5 + 6 11	5 + 7 12	5 + 8 13	5 + 9 14
6 + 0 6	6 + 1 7	6 + 2 8	6 + 3 9	6 + 4 10	6 + 5 11	6 + 6 12	6 + 7 13	6 + 8 14	6 + 9 15
7 + 0 7	7 + 1 8	7 + 2 9	7 + 3 10	7 + 4 11	7 + 5 12	7 + 6 13	7 + 7 14	7 + 8 15	7 + 9 16
8 + 0 8	8 + 1 9	8 + 2 10	8 + 3 11	8 + 4 12	8 + 5 13	8 + 6 14	8 + 7 15	8 + 8 16	8 + 9 17
9 + 0 9	9 + 1 10	9 + 2 11	9 + 3 12	9 + 4 13	9 + 5 14	9 + 6 15	9 + 7 16	9 + 8 17	9 + 9 18

LESSON
6·4

Math Boxes

1. Label the box.
Add 5 names.

15

~~HHT~~ ~~HHT~~ ~~HHT~~   20 − 5

7 + 8

Sample answers:

9 + 6   25 − 10

quince   10 + 5

1 + 14

2. What is the number?

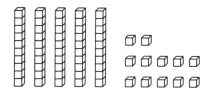

Fill in the circle next to the best answer.

(A) 37

(B) 62

(C) 512

(D) 58

3. Add.

3 + 0 = __3__

3 + 1 = __4__

  6   6
+ 0   + 1
___   ___
  6   7

4. Shade the biggest circle.

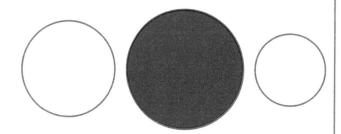

LESSON 6·5   Using the Addition/Subtraction Facts Table 2

+,−	0	1	2	3	4	5	6	7	8	9
0	0	1	2	3	4	5	6	7	8	9
1	1	2	3	4	5	6	7	8	9	10
2	2	3	4	5	6	7	8	9	10	11
3	3	4	5	6	7	8	9	10	11	12
4	4	5	6	7	8	9	10	11	12	13
5	5	6	7	8	9	10	11	12	13	14
6	6	7	8	9	10	11	12	13	14	15
7	7	8	9	10	11	12	13	14	15	16
8	8	9	10	11	12	13	14	15	16	17
9	9	10	11	12	13	14	15	16	17	18

Add or subtract. Use the table to help you.

1. $5 + 6 =$ ___11___   2. $11 - 5 =$ ___6___

3. $8 + 4 =$ ___12___   4. $12 - 4 =$ ___8___

5. $7 + 8 =$ ___15___   6. $15 - 8 =$ ___7___

7. $9 + 9 =$ ___18___   8. $18 - 9 =$ ___9___

9. $9 + 7 =$ ___16___   10. $16 - 9 =$ ___7___

LESSON 6·5   **Math Boxes**

1. Subtract.

$5 - 1 = \underline{4}$

$4 - 2 = \underline{2}$

$\underline{6} = 6 - 0$

$\underline{0} = 3 - 3$

2. Write the fact family.

$\underline{6} + \underline{5} = \underline{11}$

$\underline{5} + \underline{6} = \underline{11}$

$\underline{11} - \underline{6} = \underline{5}$

$\underline{11} - \underline{5} = \underline{6}$

3. Use your number grid.

Start at 31.

Count up 19.

You end at $\underline{50}$.

$31 + 19 = \underline{50}$

4. Draw lines to match the shapes that look alike.

Column A   Column B

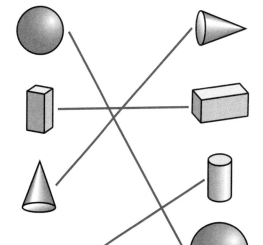

LESSON 6·6   Measuring in Centimeters

1. Use 2 longs to measure objects in centimeters.
   Record their measures in the table.

Object (name it or draw it)	My measurement
Answers vary.	about _____ cm
	about _____ cm

Use a ruler to measure to the nearest centimeter.

2. _____

   about ___15___ cm

3. _____

   about ___11___ cm

4. _____

   about ___5___ cm

5. _____

   about ___13___ cm

6. Draw a line segment that is about 9 centimeters long.

   _____

LESSON 6·6 **Fact Families and Fact Triangles**

Write the fact family for each Fact Triangle.

1.
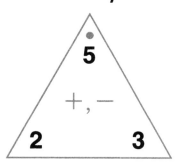

$\underline{2} + \underline{3} = \underline{5}$

$\underline{3} + \underline{2} = \underline{5}$

$\underline{5} - \underline{2} = \underline{3}$

$\underline{5} - \underline{3} = \underline{2}$

2.
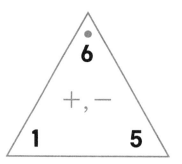

$\underline{1} + \underline{5} = \underline{6}$

$\underline{5} + \underline{1} = \underline{6}$

$\underline{6} - \underline{1} = \underline{5}$

$\underline{6} - \underline{5} = \underline{1}$

3.
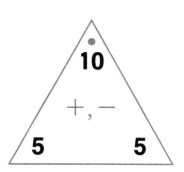

$\underline{5} + \underline{5} = \underline{10}$

$\underline{} + \underline{} = \underline{}$

$\underline{10} - \underline{5} = \underline{5}$

$\underline{} - \underline{} = \underline{}$

4. Write the missing number. Write the fact family.

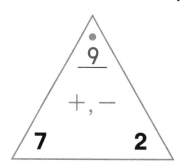

$\underline{7} + \underline{2} = \underline{9}$

$\underline{2} + \underline{7} = \underline{9}$

$\underline{9} - \underline{2} = \underline{7}$

$\underline{9} - \underline{7} = \underline{2}$

LESSON 6·6   Math Boxes

1. Write the missing numbers.

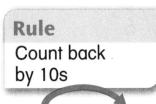

Rule
Count back
by 10s

| 44 | 34 | 24 | 14 | 4 |

2. Make a pattern. Use your Pattern-Block Template.

Answers vary.

3. Find the sums.

$6 + 1 =$ ⑦

⑨ $= 1 + 8$

$4 = 2 + 2$

$0 + 4 = 4$

Circle the odd sums.

4. Number of Siblings

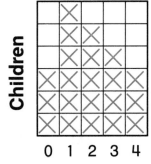

Children

0 1 2 3 4
Number of Siblings

Yes or no?

Do 4 children have exactly
2 siblings? ___no___

Do the greatest number
of children have just
1 sibling? ___yes___

LESSON 6·7   **Math Boxes**

---

1. Subtract.

$4 - 1 = \underline{3}$

$7 - 2 = \underline{5}$

$$\begin{array}{r} 5 \\ -\ 4 \\ \hline 1 \end{array} \qquad \begin{array}{r} 6 \\ -\ 0 \\ \hline 6 \end{array}$$

---

2. Write the fact family.

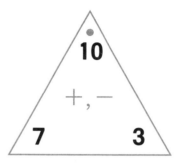

$\underline{3} + \underline{7} = \underline{10}$

$\underline{7} + \underline{3} = \underline{10}$

$\underline{10} - \underline{7} = \underline{3}$

$\underline{10} - \underline{3} = \underline{7}$

---

3. Use your number grid.

Start at 36. Count back 14.

$36 - 14 = \underline{\quad}$?

Fill in the circle next to the best answer.

(A) 50

(B) 29

(C) 18

(D) 22

---

4. Draw lines to match the shapes that look alike.

Column A   Column B

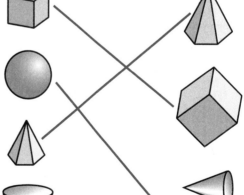

LESSON 6·8 "What's My Rule?"

1. Find the rule.

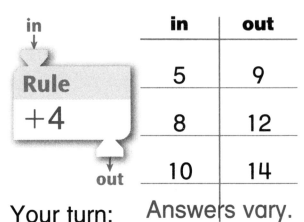

in	out
5	9
8	12
10	14

Your turn: Answers vary.

2. Fill in the blanks.

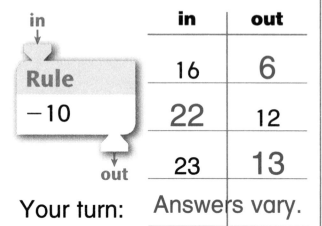

in	out
16	6
22	12
23	13

Your turn: Answers vary.

3. What comes out?

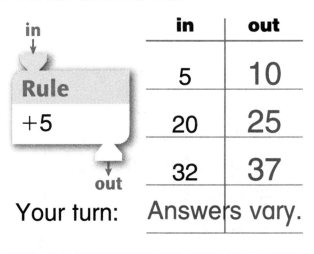

in	out
5	10
20	25
32	37

Your turn: Answers vary.

4. What goes in?

in	out
7	5
11	9
5	3

Rule −2

Your turn: Answers vary.

Make up your own. Answers vary.

5.

in → Rule → out

in	out

6.

in → Rule → out

in	out

LESSON 6·8   **Math Boxes**

---

1. Write the missing numbers.

Rule
−2

| 32 | 30 | 28 | 26 | 24 |

---

2. Draw the next two figures.

---

3. Find the sums.

7 + 1 = (8)

(10) = 2 + 8

(6) = 3 + 3

5 + 0 = 5

Circle the even sums.

4.

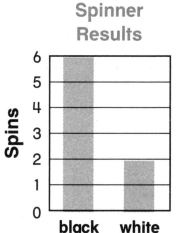

Spinner Results

How many more times did the spinner land on black than on white?

Fill in the circle next to the best answer.

Ⓐ 6   Ⓑ 2   Ⓒ 8   **Ⓓ 4**

LESSON 6·9 Counting Coins

℗ 1¢	Ⓝ 5¢	Ⓓ 10¢	Ⓠ 25¢
$0.01	$0.05	$0.10	$0.25
a penny	a nickel	a dime	a quarter

How much money? Use your coins.

1.

_____37_____ ¢

2.

_____65_____ ¢

3. Ⓠ Ⓠ Ⓓ Ⓝ Ⓝ Ⓝ Ⓝ   _____80_____ ¢

4. Ⓠ Ⓠ Ⓠ Ⓓ Ⓓ ℗ ℗   _____97_____ ¢

5. Ⓠ Ⓠ Ⓠ Ⓠ Ⓠ Ⓓ Ⓝ   _____140_____ ¢

LESSON 6·9

Math Boxes

1. Are you more likely to spin black or white?

_____white_____

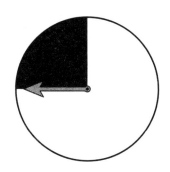

2. Measure your calculator to the nearest centimeter.

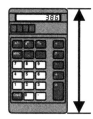

It measures about

_____ cm.

Answers vary.

3. Write the fact family.

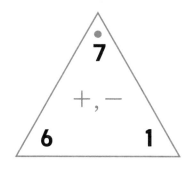

$1 + 6 = 7$

$6 + 1 = 7$

$7 - 1 = 6$

$7 - 6 = 1$

4. Shade all of the circles.

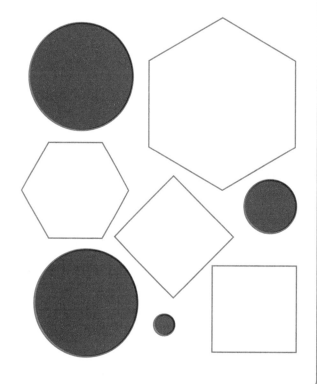

LESSON 6·10 **Time at 5-Minute Intervals**

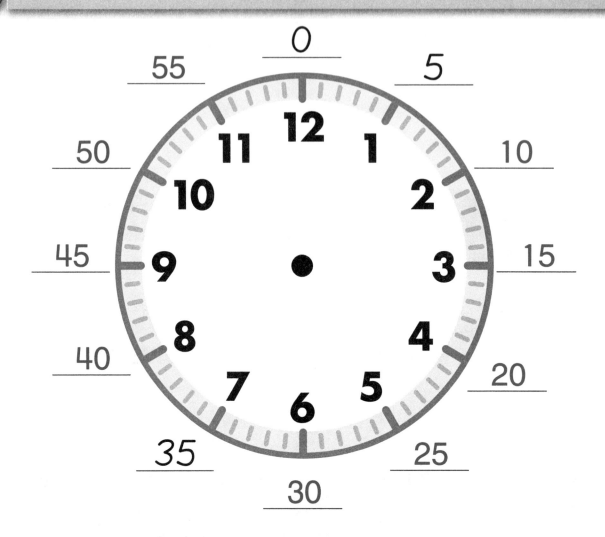

How many minutes are there in:

1. 1 hour? ___60___ minutes

2. Half an hour? ___30___ minutes

3. A quarter-hour? ___15___ minutes

4. Three-quarters of an hour? ___45___ minutes

LESSON 6·10 **Digital Notation**

Draw the hour hand and the minute hand.

1.

4:00

2.

2:30

3.

6:15

Write the time.

4.

<u>7</u> : 30

5.

<u>9</u> : 00

6.

<u>1</u> : 15

Make up your own. Draw the hour hand and minute hand.
Write the time. Answers vary.

7.
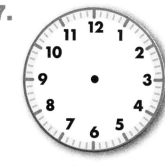

_____ : _____

8.

_____ : _____

9.

_____ : _____

LESSON 6·10   **Math Boxes**

---

1. Measure your shoe.

It measures about

_____ cm.

Answers vary.

---

2. How much money?

Ⓠ Ⓝ Ⓓ Ⓟ Ⓟ Ⓓ

_____52_____ ¢

Use Ⓟ, Ⓝ, Ⓓ, and Ⓠ to show this amount with fewer coins.

Ⓠ Ⓠ Ⓟ Ⓟ

---

3. Write <, >, or =.

Ⓝ Ⓝ **=** Ⓓ

20¢ **>** Ⓝ Ⓟ

24¢ **>** $0.18

Ⓓ Ⓓ Ⓓ **<** 40¢

---

4. Count up by 10s.

50, _____60_____, _____70_____,

_____80_____, _____90_____, _____100_____,

_____110_____, _____120_____, _____130_____

LESSON 6·11

My Reference Book Scavenger Hunt

START	Which section is about Measurement?
Turn to the Table of Contents.	Fill in the circle next to the best answer.

(A) 5th section   (B) 3rd section

(C) 4th section   **(D) 6th section**

Find 2 tools in the measurement section. Draw them.

Answers vary.

This is on page _____. | This is on page _____.

Turn to page 96.

Draw one pattern that you see.

Answers vary.

Turn to the Games Section.

Find your favorite first-grade math game.

My favorite first-grade math game is

Answers vary.
_____.

My favorite first-grade math game is on page

_____.

END

LESSON 6·11 **1- and 10-Centimeter Objects**

1. Find 3 things that are about 1 centimeter long.

   Use words or pictures to show the things you found.

   Answers vary.

2. Find 3 things that are about 10 centimeters long.

   Use words or pictures to show the things you found.

   Answers vary.

LESSON 6·11 **Math Boxes**

1. Are you more likely to spin black or white?

_____ **black** _____

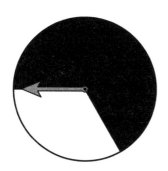

MRB 47 and 48

2. How many centimeters long is the line?

_____

Fill in the circle next to the best answer.

Ⓐ about 2 cm

Ⓑ about 3 cm

●C about 6 cm

Ⓓ about 7 cm

MRB 66

3. Write the fact family.

Total	
9	
Part	Part
9	0

__9__ + __0__ = __9__

__0__ + __9__ = __9__

__9__ − __0__ = __9__

__9__ − __9__ = __0__

MRB 25–27

4. Shade all of the squares.

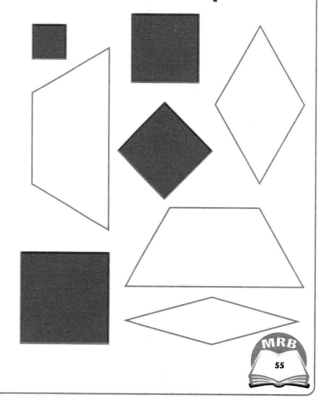

MRB 55

LESSON 6·12 Class Results of Calculator Counts

1. I counted to _____ in 15 seconds. Answers vary.

2. Class results:

Largest count	Smallest count	Range of class counts	Middle value of class counts
_____	_____	_____	_____

3. Make a bar graph of the results.

Results of Calculator Counts

Number of Children

Counted to

LESSON 6·12   **Math Boxes**

---

1. Draw a line segment that is about 7 centimeters long.

_____

MRB
66

---

2. How much money is Ⓠ Ⓠ Ⓠ Ⓟ Ⓟ Ⓟ?

Fill in the circle next to the best answer.

Ⓐ 78¢

Ⓑ 33¢

Ⓒ 73¢

Ⓓ 45¢

MRB
88 and 89

---

3. Write <, >, or =.

$7 + 6 \boxed{>} 12$

$13 \boxed{=} 6 + 7$

$14 - 6 \boxed{>} 7$

$8 \boxed{<} 15 - 6$

MRB
9

---

4. Count up by 5s.

25, __30__, __35__,

__40__, __45__, __50__,

__55__, __60__, __65__

LESSON 6·13   **Math Boxes**

---

1. Draw lines to match the shapes that look alike.

Column A   Column B

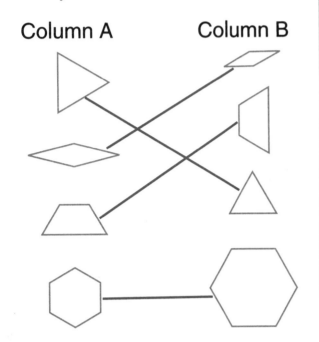

2. Shade the biggest square.

---

3. Draw lines to match the shapes that look alike.

Column A   Column B

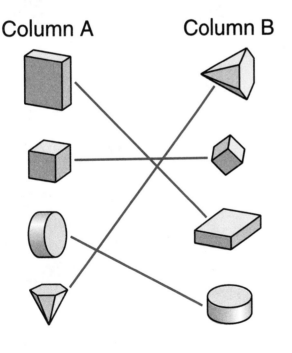

4. Shade all of the triangles.

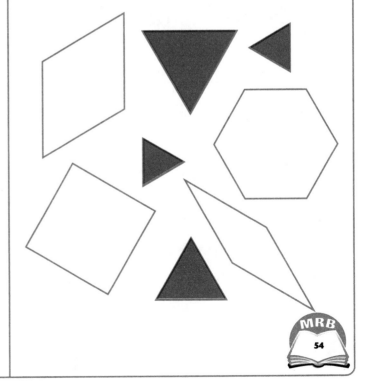

MRB
54

LESSON 7·1 *Make My Design*

Materials ☐ pattern blocks
☐ folder

Players 2

Skill Create designs using pattern blocks

Object of the Game To create a design identical to the other player's design

Directions:

1. The first player chooses 6 blocks. The second player gathers the same 6 blocks.

2. Players sit face-to-face with a folder between them.

3. The first player creates a design with the blocks.

4. Using only words, the first player tells the second player how to "Make My Design." The second player can ask questions about the instructions.

5. Players remove the folder and look at the two designs. Players discuss how closely the designs match.

6. Players change roles and play again.

LESSON 7·1 — Math Boxes

1. Shade the large shapes.

2. Find the sums.
Circle the even sums.

$$4 + 4 = \circled{8}$$

$$8 + 1 = 9$$

$$5 + 0 = \underline{\quad 5 \quad}$$

$$6 + 6 = \underline{\circled{12}}$$

MRB 96–97

3. Draw and solve.

There are 6 birds on a fence. 4 birds fly away.

How many birds are left?

___2___ birds

Sample drawing:

4. Show 53¢ in two ways.

Use Ⓠ, Ⓓ, Ⓝ, and Ⓟ.

Sample answers:

Ⓠ Ⓠ Ⓟ Ⓟ Ⓟ

or

Ⓓ Ⓓ Ⓓ Ⓓ Ⓝ Ⓝ Ⓟ Ⓟ Ⓟ

MRB 88–89

LESSON
7·2 **Math Boxes**

---

1. Draw what comes next.

☐   ☐☐   ☐☐☐   ☐☐☐☐   ☐☐☐☐☐

---

2. Subtract.

$5 - 1 = \underline{4}$ $\underline{4} = 4 - 0$

$$\begin{array}{r} 3 \\ -\,3 \\ \hline 0 \end{array}$$ $$\begin{array}{r} 6 \\ -\,1 \\ \hline 5 \end{array}$$

---

3. Draw the hands.

2:30

80–81

---

4. Complete this part of the number grid.

81	82	83
91	92	93
101	102	103
111	112	113
121	122	123

MRB
7

LESSON 7·3 **Pattern-Block Template Shapes**

1. Use your template to draw each shape.

square	large triangle	small hexagon
trapezoid	small triangle	fat rhombus
large circle	skinny rhombus	large hexagon

Date _____

2. Draw shapes that have exactly 4 sides and 4 corners. Write their names.

square
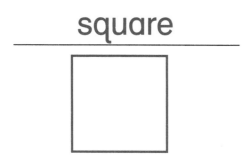

trapezoid
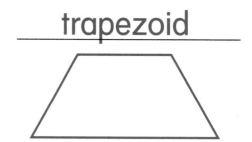

rhombus
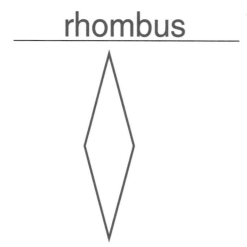

rhombus
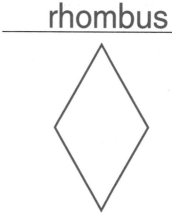

LESSON 7·3 **Math Boxes**

---

1. Find the small square.
Shade it.

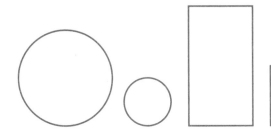

2. Find the sums.
Circle the odd sums.

$$\begin{array}{r} 3 \\ + 3 \\ \hline 6 \end{array} \qquad \begin{array}{r} 1 \\ + 4 \\ \hline \boxed{5} \end{array}$$

$$\underline{\quad 10 \quad} = 0 + 10$$

$$3 + 4 = \underline{\quad \boxed{7} \quad}$$

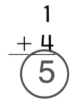

---

3. Draw and solve.

There are 8 balloons.
4 balloons pop.
How many balloons are left?

Fill in the circle next to the best answer.

○ **A.** 0   ○ **B.** 6

● **C.** 4   ○ **D.** 12

Sample drawing:

4. Show 81¢ in two ways.

Use Ⓠ, Ⓓ, Ⓝ, and Ⓟ.

Sample answers:

Ⓠ Ⓠ Ⓠ Ⓝ Ⓟ

or

Ⓠ Ⓓ Ⓓ Ⓓ Ⓓ Ⓓ Ⓝ Ⓟ

Date _____

Polygons

Triangles

4-Sided Polygons

rectangle

square

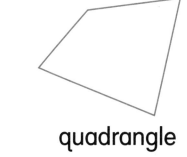

quadrangle

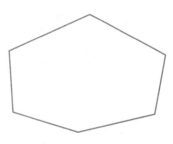

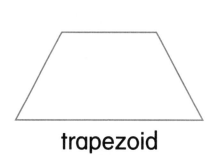

rhombus

trapezoid

Some Other Polygons

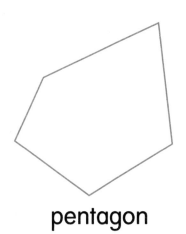

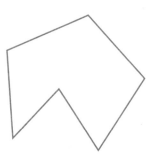

hexagon

pentagon

concave
hexagon

Math Boxes

1. Draw what comes next.

2. Subtract.

$$
\begin{array}{r} 2 \\ -\ 1 \\ \hline 1 \end{array}
\qquad
\begin{array}{r} 4 \\ -\ 4 \\ \hline 0 \end{array}
$$

$$
\begin{array}{r} 3 \\ -\ 2 \\ \hline 1 \end{array}
\qquad
\begin{array}{r} 6 \\ -\ 0 \\ \hline 6 \end{array}
$$

3. Record the time.

____8__:__15____

4. Complete this part of the number grid.

88	89	90
98	99	100
108	109	110
118	119	120
128	129	130

Date

1. Circle the name of this 3-dimensional shape.

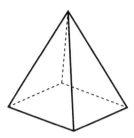

(pyramid)   prism

MRB
56

2. Circle the 4 polygons.

MRB
52–53

3.   **First-Grade Heights**

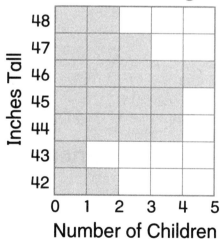

Inches Tall

48
47
46
45
44
43
42

0 1 2 3 4 5
Number of Children

Least inches tall: __42__ inches

Most inches tall: __48__ inches

MRB
44

4. Draw a line to cut the pizza in half.

Sample answer:

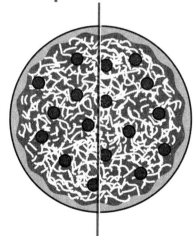

LESSON 7·6 3-Dimensional Shapes Poster

corner   flat faces

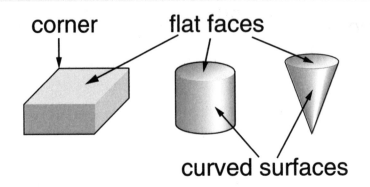

curved surfaces

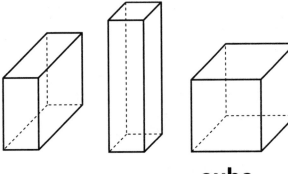

cube

rectangular prisms

sphere

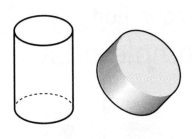

cylinders

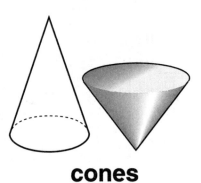

cones

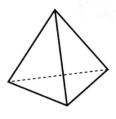 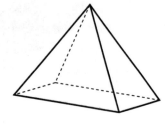 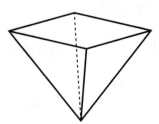 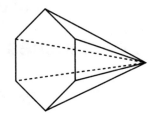

pyramids

LESSON 7·6 **Identifying 3-Dimensional Shapes**

What kind of shape is each object?
Write its name under the picture.

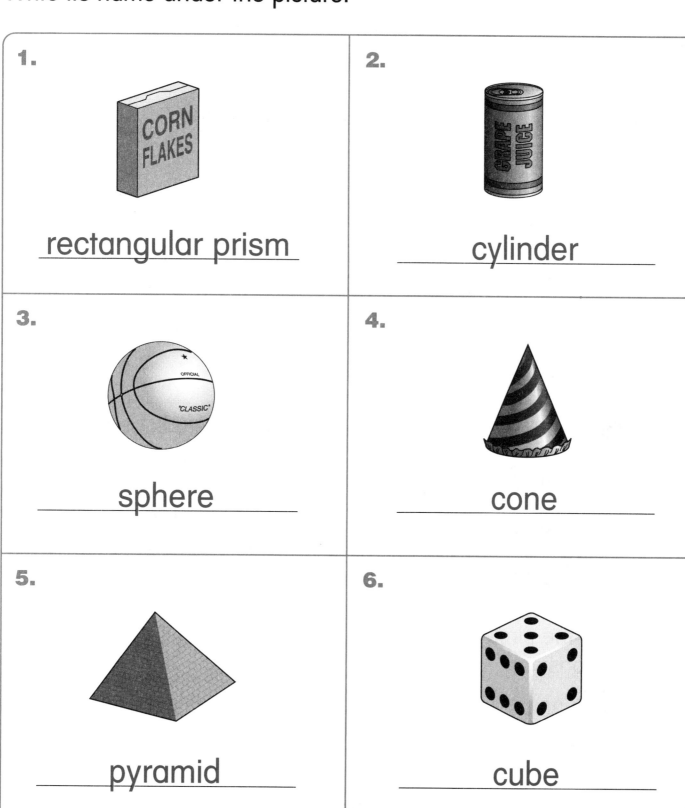

1.

rectangular prism

2.

cylinder

3.

sphere

4.

cone

5.

pyramid

6.

cube

LESSON 7·6 | **Math Boxes**

1. Draw what comes next.

  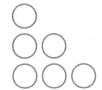 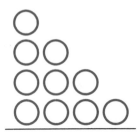

2. Subtract.

$$\begin{array}{r} 7 \\ -\ 0 \\ \hline 7 \end{array}$$

$$5 - 5 = \underline{\ \ 0\ \ }$$

$$\begin{array}{r} 5 \\ -3 \\ \hline 2 \end{array}$$

$$\begin{array}{r} 4 \\ -2 \\ \hline 2 \end{array}$$

3. What time is it?

Fill in the circle next to the best answer.

○ **A.** 9:30   ○ **B.** 6:09

○ **C.** 7:45   ● **D.** 6:45

4. Complete this part of the number grid.

104	105	106
114	115	116
124	125	126
134	135	136
144	145	146

LESSON 7·7 **Math Boxes**

1. Name or draw 3 cylinders in your classroom.

Drawings vary.

2. Name this shape.

Fill in the circle next to the best answer.

○ **A.** rhombus

○ **B.** trapezoid

● **C.** hexagon

○ **D.** square

 MRB 54–55

3.

First-Grade Heights

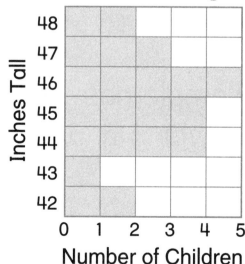

Inches Tall

48 47 46 45 44 43 42

0 1 2 3 4 5
Number of Children

What is the middle value?

About ___45___ inches

 MRB 46

4. Draw a line to cut the cookie in half.

Sample answer:

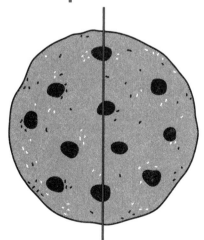

LESSON 7·8 Math Boxes

1. Divide each shape in half.

Sample answers:

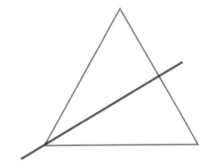

2. Complete this part of the number grid.

123	124	125
133	134	135
143	144	145
153	154	155
163	164	165

3. How much money?

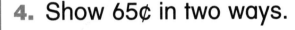

Ⓠ Ⓝ Ⓓ Ⓝ Ⓓ Ⓟ Ⓝ

61 ¢

Use Ⓠ, Ⓓ, Ⓝ, and Ⓟ to show this amount with fewer coins.

Sample answer:

Ⓠ Ⓠ Ⓓ Ⓟ

4. Show 65¢ in two ways.

Use Ⓠ, Ⓓ, Ⓝ, and Ⓟ.

Sample answers:

Ⓠ Ⓠ Ⓓ Ⓝ

or

Ⓓ Ⓓ Ⓓ Ⓓ Ⓓ Ⓝ Ⓝ Ⓝ

MRB
88–89

MRB
88–89

Date _____

How Much Money?

Record the amount shown.

1.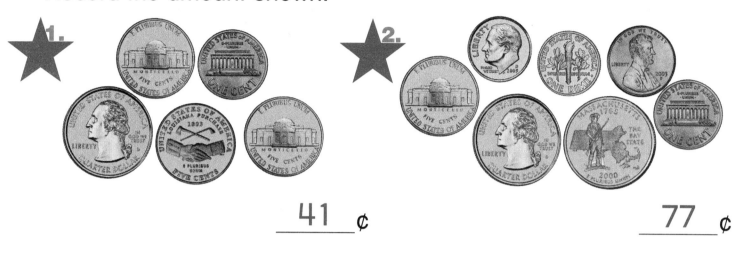

_____41_____ ¢

2.

_____77_____ ¢

Mark the coins you need to buy each item. Sample answers:

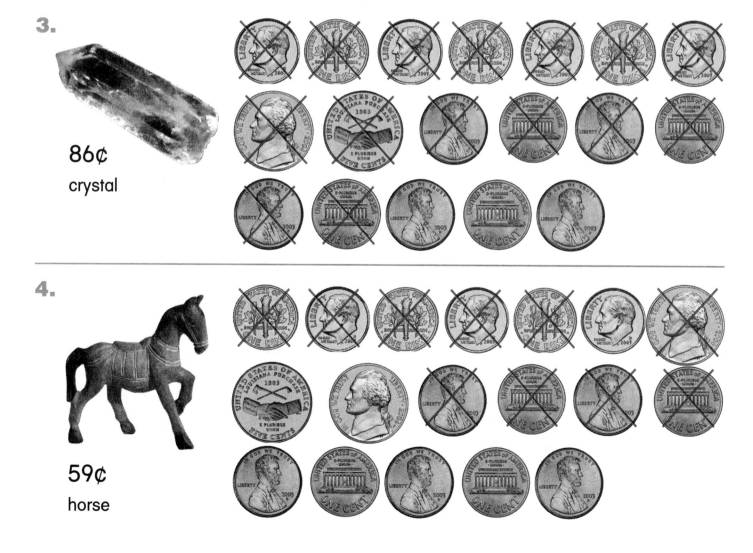

3.

86¢
crystal

4.

59¢
horse

LESSON
8·1

Time

Draw the hands.

1.

$$10:00$$

2.

$$6:30$$

3.

$$1:45$$

4.

$$8:15$$

5.

$$11:05$$

6.

$$2:35$$

Date _____

1. How much money?

Q Q Q Q Q D P

_____136_____ ¢ or

$ _____1.36_____

MRB 88–90

2. Draw a line to match each face to the correct picture of the 3-dimensional shape.

Column A   Column B

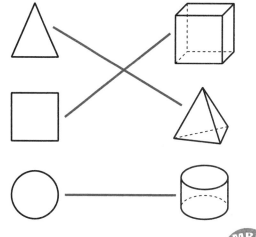

MRB 58

3. Add.

```
   7          2
 + 3        + 6
 ----       ----
  10          8


   2          8
 + 2        + 1
 ----       ----
   4          9
```

4. Use your number grid.

Start at 59.

Count back 20.

_____39_____ = 59 − 20

MRB 32

Comparing Money Amounts

LESSON 8·2

Write <, >, or =.

> < is less than
> = is equal to
> > is greater than

1. 2 dimes $\boxed{<}$ $0.25

2. 50¢ $\boxed{>}$ 5 pennies

3. 4 quarters $\boxed{=}$ 100¢

4. 100¢ $\boxed{=}$ 20 nickels

5. $1.25 $\boxed{>}$ 120¢

6. $1.75 $\boxed{=}$ 7 quarters

7. 200¢ $\boxed{>}$ 10 dimes and 10 nickels

8. $1.44 $\boxed{=}$ 1 dollar, 4 dimes, and 4 pennies

LESSON 8·2 **Math Boxes**

---

1. Use  $1, Q, D, N, and P to show this amount.

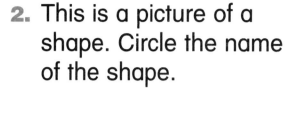

$3.49

Sample answer.

$1 $1 $1 Q D N N
P P P P

MRB 88–90

---

2. This is a picture of a shape. Circle the name of the shape.

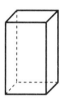

(prism)   pyramid

MRB 56–57

---

3. Subtract.

```
   6          5
 − 3        − 4
 ───        ───
   3          1


   9          3
 − 1        − 3
 ───        ───
   8          0
```

---

4. Add.

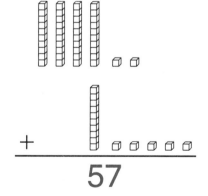

```
+        
─────────
   57
```

MRB 28

LESSON 8·3 Hundreds, Tens, and Ones Riddles

Hundreds	Tens	Ones

Solve the riddles. Use your base-10 blocks to help you.

Example: 2 ☐ 3 ▯ 5 ◻

What am I? __235__

1. 7 ▯ 2 ◻

What am I? ___72___

2. 2 ☐ 3 ▯ 4 ◻

What am I? ___234___

3. 8 hundreds, 5 tens, and 2 ones

What am I? ___852___

4. 4 hundreds and 6 ones

What am I? ___406___

Try This

5. 2 hundreds, 14 tens, and 5 ones. What am I? ___345___

6. 12 ones, 7 tens, and 3 hundreds. What am I? ___382___

7. Make up your own riddle. Ask a friend to solve it.
Answers vary.

LESSON 8·3   Math Boxes

1. Count the coins.

Q Q Q N P P P

Choose the best answer.

- Ⓐ 38¢
- Ⓑ 88¢
- Ⓒ 93¢
- **Ⓓ** 83¢

MRB 88–90

2. Draw a line to match each face to the correct picture of the 3-dimensional shape.

Column A   Column B

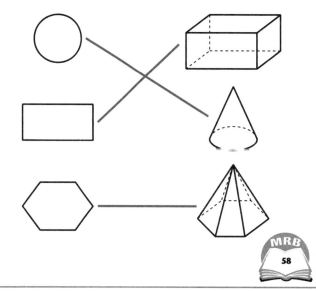

MRB 58

3. Add.

$$\begin{array}{r} 5 \\ + 5 \\ \hline 10 \end{array} \qquad \begin{array}{r} 7 \\ + 2 \\ \hline 9 \end{array}$$

$$\begin{array}{r} 1 \\ + 4 \\ \hline 5 \end{array} \qquad \begin{array}{r} 2 \\ + 3 \\ \hline 5 \end{array}$$

4. Use your number grid.

Start at 71.

Count up 19.

71 + 19 = ___90___

MRB 29

LESSON 8·4 School Store Mini-Poster 2

crayon
6¢

scissors
32¢

ball
35¢

gum
2¢

pencil
28¢

candy
8¢

eraser
17¢

Date

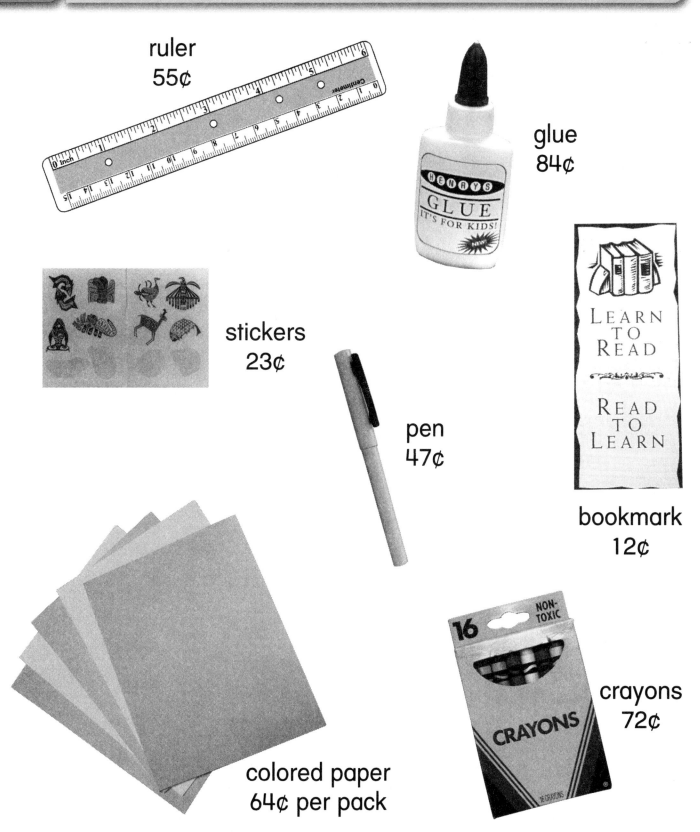

ruler
55¢

glue
84¢

stickers
23¢

pen
47¢

LEARN
TO
READ

READ
TO
LEARN

bookmark
12¢

colored paper
64¢ per pack

crayons
72¢

LESSON 8·4 Number Stories

Sample Story

I bought a and an . I paid 52 cents.

Number model: 35¢ + 17¢ = 52¢

Answers vary.

1. Story 1

Number model: _____

2. Story 2

Number model: _____

LESSON 8·4 — **Math Boxes**

1. $1.00 =

___100___ pennies

___20___ nickels

___10___ dimes

___4___ quarters

2. Name or draw 2 objects shaped like a rectangular prism. **Answers vary.**

MRB 88–90

MRB 56–57

3. Subtract.

$$\begin{array}{r} 4 \\ -\ 2 \\ \hline 2 \end{array} \qquad \begin{array}{r} 7 \\ -\ 1 \\ \hline 6 \end{array}$$

$$\begin{array}{r} 6 \\ -\ 0 \\ \hline 6 \end{array} \qquad \begin{array}{r} 10 \\ -\ 5 \\ \hline 5 \end{array}$$

4. What is the sum?

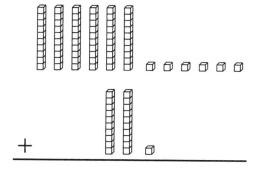

Choose the best answer.

Ⓐ 45 　　Ⓑ **87**

Ⓒ 85 　　Ⓓ 78

MRB 28

LESSON 8·5

Museum Store Mini-Poster

seashell
48¢

kite
$1.86

elephant
72¢

rock
35¢

horse
59¢

ring
18¢

magnet
$1.39

puzzle
85¢

plane
27¢

LESSON 8·5 Making Change

Record what you bought. Record how much change you got.

Example:

I bought _____*a plane*_____ for __27__ cents.

I gave _____Ⓓ Ⓓ Ⓓ_____
to the clerk.

I got _____Ⓟ Ⓟ Ⓟ_____ in change.

Answers vary.

1. I bought _____ for _____ cents.

   I gave _____ to the clerk.

   I got _____ in change.

2. I bought _____ for _____ cents.

   I gave _____ to the clerk.

   I got _____ in change.

3. I bought _____ for _____ cents.

   I gave _____ to the clerk.

   I got _____ in change.

LESSON 8·5

Math Boxes

---

1. Circle the tens place.

3⑥   1②0   ⑤9

⑥6   ②0   10④

MRB 10

2. Keisha bought a ball for 25¢.

She bought a bat for 75¢.

How much did Keisha pay?

___100___ ¢ or $___1.00___

---

3. Draw the other half.

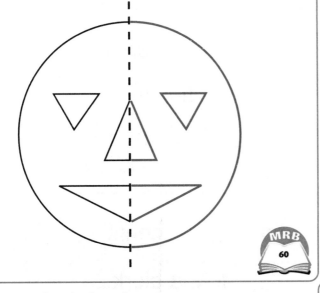

MRB 60

4. Draw a polygon with 6 sides.

Answers vary.

MRB 52–53

---

5. Label the box.
Add 3 new names.

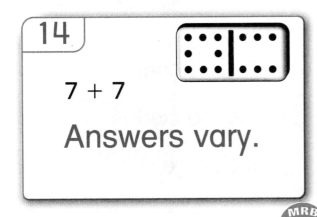

14

7 + 7

Answers vary.

MRB 16

6. Subtract.

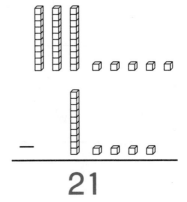

21

MRB 31

LESSON 8·6 Equal Shares

Show how you share your crackers. See children's work.

1 cracker, 2 people

Halves

1 cracker, 4 people

Fourths

1 cracker, 3 people

Thirds

2 crackers, 4 people

LESSON 8·6   **"What's My Rule?"**

Write the rule. Complete the table.

1. in → Rule **+10** → out

in	out
23	33
15	25
7	17
37	47

2. in → Rule **−10** → out

in	out
13	3
51	41
18	8
29	19

3. in → Rule **−20** → out

in	out
45	25
21	1
70	50
57	37

4. in → Rule **+20** → out

in	out
12	32
28	48
30	50
45	65

Make up your own. Answers vary.

5.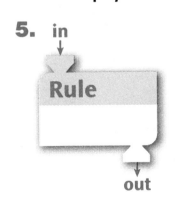

in	out

6.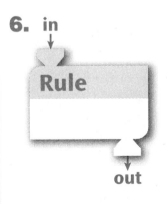

in	out

LESSON 8·6   **Math Boxes**

1. A ring costs 20¢.

I pay a 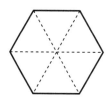.

How much change will I get?

_____5_____ ¢

2. How many equal parts?

Choose the best answer.

(A) 8   (B) 1   **(C) 6**   (D) 2   MRB 12

3. What number are you most likely to spin?

___2___

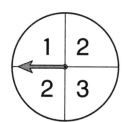

MRB 47–48

4. Write the fact family.

$\underline{5} + \underline{9} = \underline{14}$
$\underline{9} + \underline{5} = \underline{14}$
$\underline{14} - \underline{9} = \underline{5}$
$\underline{14} - \underline{5} = \underline{9}$

MRB 25

5. Complete the graph.

5 children take the bus.
3 children ride bikes.

Ways to School

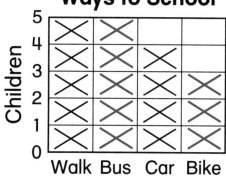

MRB 44

6. Use <, >, or =.

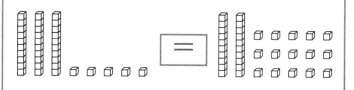

MRB 9, 11

LESSON 8·7 Equal Parts of Wholes

Which glass is half full? Circle it.

Which rectangles are divided into thirds? Circle them.

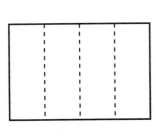

A

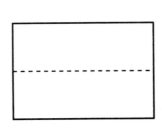

B

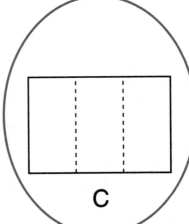

C

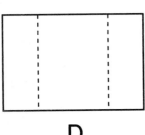

D

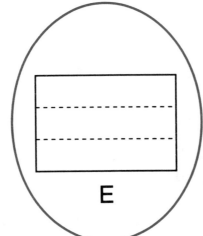

E

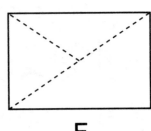

F

LESSON 8·7 **Fractions**

1. How many equal parts are there? _____3_____

   Write a fraction in each part of the circle.

   Color $\frac{1}{3}$ of the circle.

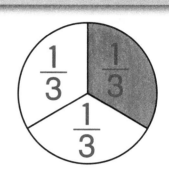

2. How many equal parts are there? _____4_____

   Write a fraction in each part of the square.

   Color $\frac{1}{4}$ of the square.

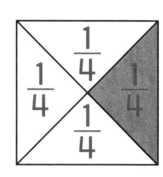

3. How many equal parts are there? _____6_____

   Write a fraction in each part of the hexagon.

   Color $\frac{1}{6}$ of the hexagon.

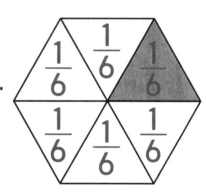

4. How many equal parts are there? _____8_____

   Write a fraction in each part of the rectangle.

   Color $\frac{1}{8}$ of the rectangle.

LESSON 8·7 Math Boxes

1. Circle the hundreds place.

(2)89   (3)00   (1)12

(7)33   (9)99   (2)05

MRB 10

2. Carlos bought 3 pencils. Each pencil costs 10¢. How much did Carlos pay?

___30___ ¢ or $ _0.30_

3. Draw the other half.

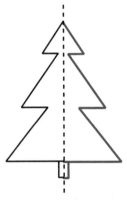

MRB 60

4. Use a straightedge.

Draw line segments to make a polygon.

Answers vary.

MRB 52–53

5. Label the box.
Add 3 new names.

8   (N)(P)(P)(P)

18 − 10

Answers vary.

MRB 16

6. Subtract.

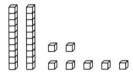

21

MRB 31

Date _____

Sharing Pennies

Use your pennies to help you solve the problems.

Circle each person's share.

1. Halves: 2 people share 8 pennies equally.

   How many pennies does each person get? __4__ pennies

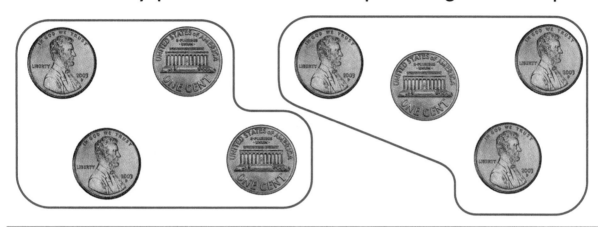

2. Thirds: 3 people share 9 pennies equally.

   How many pennies does each person get? __3__ pennies

   How many pennies do 2 of the 3 people get in all?

   __6__ pennies

LESSON 8·8

Sharing Pennies *continued*

3. Fifths: 5 people share 15 pennies equally.

How many pennies does each person get? __3__ pennies

How many pennies do 3 of the 5 people get in all?

__9__ pennies

4. Fourths: 4 people share 20 pennies.

How many pennies does each person get? __5__ pennies

How many pennies do 2 of the 4 people get in all?

__10__ pennies

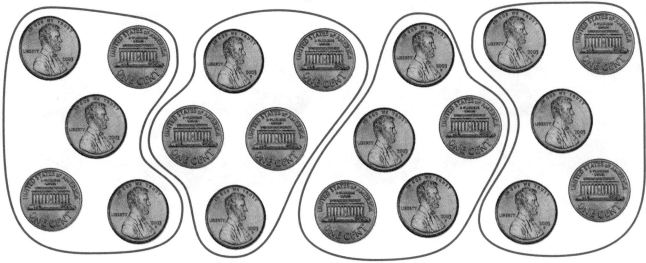

LESSON 8·8 Math Boxes

1. A seashell costs $0.48.
I pay 2 Ⓠ.

How much change will
I get?

___2___ ¢

2. Label each equal part.

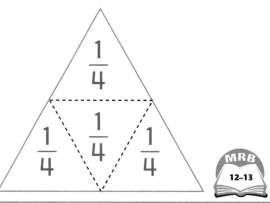

$\frac{1}{4}$

$\frac{1}{4}$ $\frac{1}{4}$ $\frac{1}{4}$

MRB 12–13

3. Complete the graph.

5 children live 6 blocks away.
4 children live 7 blocks away.

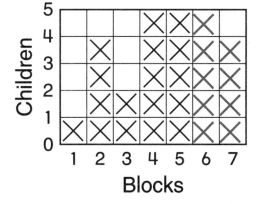

Blocks from School

MRB 44

4. Write the fact family.

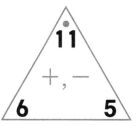

11

+, −

6   5

___6___ + ___5___ = ___11___

___5___ + ___6___ = ___11___

___11___ − ___5___ = ___6___

___11___ − ___6___ = ___5___

MRB 27

5. What number are you
most likely to spin?

___3___

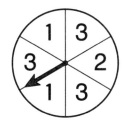

MRB 47–48

6. Write <, >, or =.

13 $\boxed{<}$ 31

108 $\boxed{>}$ 80

1 + 2 $\boxed{<}$ 12

MRB 9

LESSON 8·9

Math Boxes

---

1. Circle the ones place.

36④   58⑧   100⑩

④   16⑥   222⑳

MRB 10

---

2. You buy 2 packs of seeds. Each pack costs 60¢.

How much do you pay?

___120___ ¢ or $___1.20___

---

3. Divide each shape in half. Shade one half of each shape.

Sample answers:

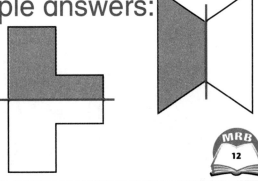

MRB 12

---

4. Name this polygon.

Choose the best answer.

Ⓐ hexagon   Ⓑ square

Ⓒ rhombus   **Ⓓ** trapezoid

MRB 54–55

---

5. Write 3 more names.

100

80 + 20

Answers vary.

MRB 16

---

6. Subtract.

3

MRB 31

LESSON 8·10

Math Boxes

---

1. Use <, >, or =.

$\text{Q} \text{Q}$ $\boxed{>}$ $0.25

$1.00 $\boxed{>}$ $\text{Q} \text{D} \text{Q} \text{D}$

10¢ + 20¢ $\boxed{=}$ $\text{N} \text{Q}$

MRB 9, 88–90

---

2. Use your number grid.

Start at 33.
Count back 9.

$$\begin{array}{r} 33 \\ -\ 9 \\ \hline 24 \end{array}$$

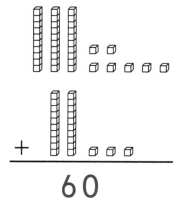
MRB 32

---

3. Subtract.

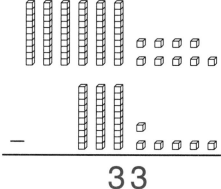

$$33$$

MRB 31

---

4. Add.

$$60$$

MRB 28

---

5. Solve.

$3 + 4 =$ ___7___

___8___ $= 2 + 6$

___4___ $= 5 - 1$

$6 - 3 =$ ___3___

---

6. Write 3 names.

$1.00

Answers vary.

MRB 16

LESSON 9·1 Number-Grid Hunt

0	10	20	30	40	50	60	70	80	90	100	110
-1	9	19	29	39	49	59	69	79	89	99	109
-2	8	18	28	38	48	58	68	78	88	98	108
-3	7	17	27	37	47	57	67	77	87	97	107
-4	6	16	26	36	46	56	66	76	86	96	106
-5	5	15	25	35	45	55	65	75	85	95	105
-6	4	14	24	34	44	54	64	74	84	94	104
-7	3	13	23	33	43	53	63	73	83	93	103
-8	2	12	22	32	42	52	62	72	82	92	102
-9	1	11	21	31	41	51	61	71	81	91	101

LESSON 9·1 | **Math Boxes**

1. Use your number grid.
Start at 26.
Count up 14.

$$\begin{array}{r} 26 \\ + 14 \\ \hline 40 \end{array}$$

MRB 29

2. Shade $\frac{1}{4}$ of the circle.

MRB 13

3. Fill in the missing numbers.

Rule

Add 5

in	out
8	13
12	17
29	34
41	46
100	105

MRB 100–102

4. Write the fact family.

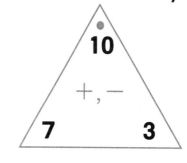

$$\underline{}7\underline{} + \underline{}3\underline{} = \underline{}10\underline{}$$
$$\underline{}3\underline{} + \underline{}7\underline{} = \underline{}10\underline{}$$
$$\underline{}10\underline{} - \underline{}7\underline{} = \underline{}3\underline{}$$
$$\underline{}10\underline{} - \underline{}3\underline{} = \underline{}7\underline{}$$

MRB 27

5. Tell the time.

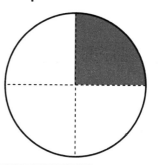

7 : 20

MRB 81

6. Freddy has Ⓠ Ⓓ Ⓓ Ⓝ.
Jewel has Ⓓ Ⓓ Ⓝ Ⓓ Ⓓ Ⓟ.

Who has more money?

Freddy

How much more money?

4 ¢

LESSON 9·2   *Number-Grid Game*

Materials
- ☐ a number grid
- ☐ a die
- ☐ a game marker for each player

Players   2 or more

Skill   Counting on the number grid

Object of the Game   To land on 110 with an exact roll

1. Players put their markers at 0 on the number grid.

2. Take turns. When it is your turn:
   ◆ Roll the die.
   ◆ Use the table to see how many spaces to move your marker.
   ◆ Move your marker that many spaces.

3. Continue playing. The winner is the first player to get to 110 with an exact roll.

Roll	Spaces
⚀	1 or 10
⚁	2 or 20
⚂	3
⚃	4
⚄	5
⚅	6

LESSON 9·2   Math Boxes

---

1. Use your number grid.
Start at 90.
Count back 25.

$$\begin{array}{r} 90 \\ -\ 25 \\ \hline 65 \end{array}$$

2. Find the sums.

$2 + 5 = \underline{\ 7\ }$

$12 + 5 = \underline{\ 17\ }$

$42 + 5 = \underline{\ 47\ }$

$102 + 5 = \underline{\ 107\ }$

---

3. Shade $\frac{1}{2}$ of the pennies.

Ⓟ Ⓟ Ⓟ Ⓟ Ⓟ

Ⓟ Ⓟ Ⓟ Ⓟ Ⓟ

4. Asha bought a key chain for 43¢.

She paid Ⓠ Ⓠ.

How much change did she get? __7__ ¢

Show this amount with Ⓓ, Ⓝ, and Ⓟ. Sample answer:

Ⓝ Ⓟ Ⓟ

---

5. Fill in the missing numbers.

Rule						
−1	653	652	651	650	649	648

---

6. Circle the four polygons.

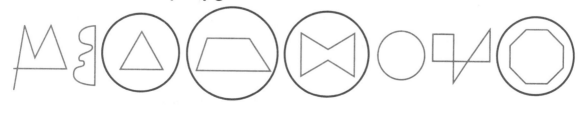

LESSON 9·3 Number-Grid Puzzles 1

0	10	20	30	40		60	70	80	90	100	110
	9										
						68	78	88			
	7	17	27	37		67					
						66		86			
	5							85			
	4			44	54	64	74	84		104	
	3	23						83		103	
	2	22	32	42	52		72			102	
		21				61			91	101	

LESSON 9·3

Math Boxes

1. Use your number grid.
   Start at 36.
   Count up 22.

   36 + 22 = __58__

   MRB 29

2. Divide the rhombus in half.
   Shade $\frac{1}{2}$.

   Sample answer:

   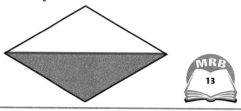

   MRB 13

3. Find the rule and the missing numbers.

   in

   Rule
   −10

   out

in	out
15	5
21	11
84	74
104	94

   MRB 100–102

4. Write the fact family.

   __6__ + __9__ = __15__

   __9__ + __6__ = __15__

   __15__ − __6__ = __9__

   __15__ − __9__ = __6__

   MRB 27

5. What time is it?

   Fill in the circle next to the best answer

   Ⓐ 2:20

   Ⓑ 4:02

   Ⓒ 4:10

   Ⓓ 2:04

   MRB 81

6. Jonah has .

   Mari has .

   Who has more money?
   __Mari__

   How much more money?
   __8__ ¢

Date _____

Silly Animal Stories

Example:

Unit
inches

koala
24 in.

penguin
36 in.

How tall are the koala and penguin together?

24 + 36 = 60

60 *inches*

---

1. Silly Story

Unit

Answers vary.

---

2. Silly Story

Unit

LESSON 9·4 **Math Boxes**

1. Use your number grid.
Start at 48. Count back 15.
48 − 15 = ?
Fill in the circle next to the best answer.

Ⓐ 43   ⬤ 33

Ⓒ 63   Ⓓ 36

 MRB 32

2. Solve.

$16 - 9 = \underline{7}$

$26 - 9 = \underline{17}$

$56 - 9 = \underline{47}$

$106 - 9 = \underline{97}$

3. Draw 12 dimes.
Use Ⓓs.

Shade $\frac{1}{4}$ of the dimes.

MRB 14

4. A toy dinosaur costs 89¢.

I paid $1.00.

How much change do I get?

$\underline{11}$ ¢

Show this amount with Ⓓ, Ⓝ, and Ⓟ.

Sample answer: Ⓓ Ⓟ

5. Find the rule. Fill in the missing numbers.

MRB 98, 99

Rule					
Add 100	165	265	365	465	565

6. Circle the 3 polygons.

  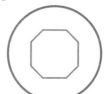

MRB 52, 53

LESSON 9·5 — My Height Record

First Measurement

Date _____

Height: about _____ inches

A typical height for a first grader in my class was about

_____ inches.

Answers vary.

Second Measurement

Date _____

Height: about _____ inches

A typical height for a first grader in my class is about

_____ inches.

The middle height for my class is about _____ inches.

Change to Height

I grew about _____ inches.

The typical growth in my class was about _____ inches.

Date _____

1. Find the sums.

$2 + 6 =$ _____ 8

$20 + 60 =$ _____ 80

$200 + 600 =$ _____ 800

2. Complete the number-grid puzzle.

21	22	
	32	33
	42	
51		

MRB 7

3. Label each part.

Shade $\frac{1}{3}$ of the rectangle.

| $\frac{1}{3}$ | $\frac{1}{3}$ | $\frac{1}{3}$ |

MRB 13

4. Circle the 4 letters that are symmetrical.

Ⓐ P Ⓗ Ⓔ

L Ⓥ F Q

MRB 60

5. Myla buys 2 items at the store.

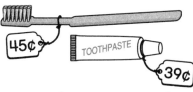

How much money does she spend?

84¢

Show this amount with
Ⓠ, Ⓓ, Ⓝ, and Ⓟ.
Sample answer:
Ⓠ Ⓠ Ⓠ Ⓝ Ⓟ Ⓟ Ⓟ Ⓟ

6. This is a picture of a 3-D shape.
Circle the name of the shape.

pyramid   (cone)

MRB 56, 57

LESSON 9·6 **Pattern-Block Fractions**

Use pattern blocks to divide each shape into equal parts.
Draw the parts using your Pattern-Block Template.
Shade parts of the shapes.

1. Divide the rhombus into halves. Shade $\frac{1}{2}$ of the rhombus.

2. Divide the trapezoid into thirds. Shade $\frac{2}{3}$ of the trapezoid.

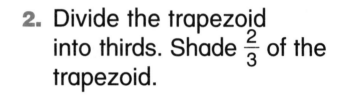

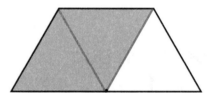

3. Divide the hexagon into halves. Shade $\frac{2}{2}$ of the hexagon.

4. Divide the hexagon into thirds. Shade $\frac{2}{3}$ of the hexagon.

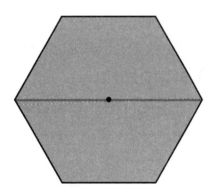

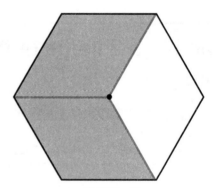

5. Divide the hexagon into sixths. Shade $\frac{4}{6}$ of the hexagon.

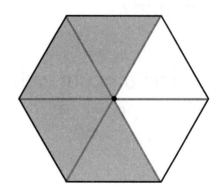

Date _____

1. Solve.

$$\underline{\quad 18 \quad} = 9 + 9$$

$$\underline{\quad 180 \quad} = 90 + 90$$

$$\begin{array}{r} 7 \\ -\ 5 \\ \hline 2 \end{array} \qquad \begin{array}{r} 70 \\ -\ 50 \\ \hline 20 \end{array} \qquad \begin{array}{r} 700 \\ -\ 500 \\ \hline 200 \end{array}$$

2. Divide the rectangle into fourths. Shade $\frac{3}{4}$ of the rectangle.

Sample answer:

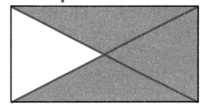

MRB 12, 13

3. Draw and solve.

Griffin had 14 guppies.

He gave $\frac{1}{2}$ away.

How many guppies are left?

$\underline{\quad 7 \quad}$ guppies

MRB 14

4. Write the numbers.

$\underline{175}$

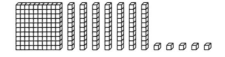

$\underline{242}$

MRB 10, 11

5. **Weekly Allowance**

MRB 44

Smallest allowance: $\underline{1.00}$

Largest allowance: $\underline{5.00}$

6. Record the temperature.

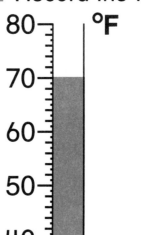

$\underline{\quad 70 \quad}$ °F

Odd or even?

$\underline{\text{even}}$

MRB 87, 97

LESSON 9·7 Fraction Strips

Use your fraction strips to compare the fractions.

< is less than

> is greater than

= is equal to

Unit

1-strip

1. $\dfrac{1}{2}$ $\boxed{>}$ $\dfrac{1}{4}$

2. $\dfrac{1}{8}$ $\boxed{<}$ $\dfrac{1}{4}$

3. $\dfrac{1}{2}$ $\boxed{>}$ $\dfrac{1}{8}$

4. $\dfrac{1}{2}$ $\boxed{>}$ $\dfrac{1}{3}$

5. $\dfrac{1}{6}$ $\boxed{<}$ $\dfrac{1}{3}$

6. $\dfrac{1}{4}$ $\boxed{<}$ $\dfrac{1}{3}$

7. $\dfrac{1}{4}$ $\boxed{>}$ $\dfrac{1}{6}$

8. $\dfrac{1}{2}$ $\boxed{>}$ $\dfrac{1}{6}$

Try This

9. $\dfrac{1}{2}$ $\boxed{<}$ $\dfrac{2}{3}$

10. $\dfrac{2}{4}$ $\boxed{=}$ $\dfrac{1}{2}$

Date _____

1. Solve.

$7 - 4 =$ ___3___

$70 - 40 =$ ___30___

$700 - 400 =$ ___300___

2. Complete the number-grid puzzle.

58	59	60
		70
	79	
88	89	

3. Label each part. Shade $\frac{5}{6}$ of the hexagon.

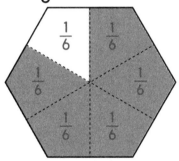

MRB 13

4. Circle the 3 numbers that are symmetrical.

1 6 3

0 5 4

MRB 60

5. Diego buys 2 items at the store.

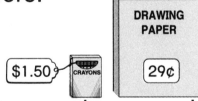

$1.50 CRAYONS   DRAWING PAPER 29¢

How much money does he spend?
$ ___1.79___

Show this amount with $1, Q, D, N, and P.
Sample answer: $1 Q Q
D D N P P P P

6. This is a picture of a 3-dimensional shape. Name the shape.

Fill in the circle next to the best answer.

(A) sphere (B) cube

(C) cylinder (D) cone

MRB 56, 57

Date _____

Many Names for Fractions

1-strip

Use your fraction pieces to help you solve the following problems.

Example:

$\underline{4}$ $\boxed{\dfrac{1}{8}}$ $=$ $\boxed{\dfrac{1}{2}}$

$\dfrac{4}{8} = \dfrac{1}{2}$

1.

$\underline{2}$ $\boxed{\dfrac{1}{6}}$ $=$ $\boxed{\dfrac{1}{3}}$

$\dfrac{2}{6} = \dfrac{1}{3}$

2.

$\underline{2}$ $\boxed{\dfrac{1}{8}}$ $=$ $\boxed{\dfrac{1}{4}}$

$\dfrac{2}{8} = \dfrac{1}{4}$

LESSON 9·8

Many Names for Fractions *continued*

3.

$\dfrac{4}{}$

$\dfrac{1}{6}$	=	$\dfrac{1}{3}$	$\dfrac{1}{3}$

$$\dfrac{4}{6} = \dfrac{2}{3}$$

4.

$\dfrac{4}{}$

$\dfrac{1}{8}$	=	$\dfrac{1}{4}$	$\dfrac{1}{4}$

$$\dfrac{4}{8} = \dfrac{2}{4}$$

5.

$\dfrac{6}{}$

$\dfrac{1}{8}$	=	$\dfrac{1}{4}$	$\dfrac{1}{4}$	$\dfrac{1}{4}$

$$\dfrac{6}{8} = \dfrac{3}{4}$$

LESSON 9·8

Math Boxes

1. Solve.

$$\frac{4}{} = 9 - 5$$

$$\frac{40}{} = 90 - 50$$

$$\begin{array}{c} 6 \\ + 4 \\ \hline 10 \end{array} \qquad \begin{array}{c} 60 \\ + 40 \\ \hline 100 \end{array} \qquad \begin{array}{c} 600 \\ + 400 \\ \hline 1000 \end{array}$$

2. What fraction is shaded?
Fill in the circle next to the best answer.

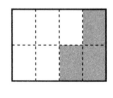

Ⓐ $\frac{1}{3}$ **Ⓑ** $\frac{3}{8}$

Ⓒ $\frac{8}{3}$ Ⓓ $\frac{3}{1}$

3. Draw and solve.
Emma had 15 grapes.
She gave $\frac{1}{3}$ to her sister.
How many grapes did her sister get?

____5____ grapes

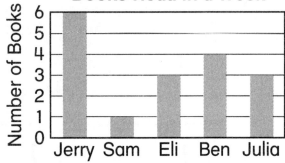

4. Write the numbers.

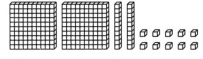

____230____

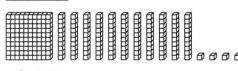

____214____

5.

Books Read in a Week

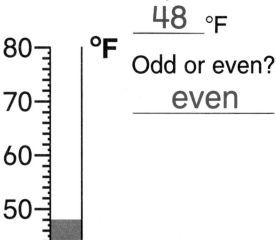

Number of Books — Jerry Sam Eli Ben Julia

Fewest number of books read: ____1____
Greatest number of books read: ____6____
Range: ____5____

6. Record the temperature.

____48____ °F

Odd or even?

____even____

Date _____

LESSON
9·9 **Math Boxes**

1. Lowest count:
___15___

Highest count:
___20___

Range:
___5___

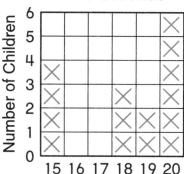
Calculator Counts in 15 Seconds

MRB 44, 45

2. Sam buys 2 items at the store.

How much money does he spend?
__$3.40 or 340¢__

Show this amount with $1,
Q, D, N, and P.
Sample answer:
$1 $1 $1 Q D N

MRB 88–90

3. You have $1.00. You buy a pretzel that costs 75¢.

How much change do you get?
__25__¢

Show this amount with Q, D, N, and P.
Sample answer: Q

4. Pedro has Q D N P N N D. Claudia has D D N Q N Q P.

Who has more money?
____Claudia____

How much more money?
__20__¢

5. Use a ruler. Draw a polygon with 4 sides.
Answers vary.

MRB 52–53

6. Draw the hands.

9:35

MRB 81

one hundred ninety-three **193**

LESSON 10·1

Math Boxes

1. Record the temperatures.

Temperatures
Recorded This Month

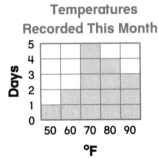

Coolest temperature:

__50__ °F

Warmest temperature: __90__ °F

Range: __40__ °F

 MRB 44–45

2. How much money does Kylie have?

Ⓠ Ⓠ Ⓝ Ⓓ Ⓓ Ⓓ Ⓓ

$__0__.__95__

How much money does Pete have? Ⓠ Ⓠ Ⓓ Ⓠ Ⓠ

$__1__.__10__

Who has more money?

__Pete__

How much more money?

$__0__.__15__

3. Draw a triangle with one side that is 1 inch long.

Sample answer:

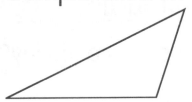

MRB 54

4. Circle the bigger fraction.

$\frac{2}{6}$ $\frac{1}{2}$

MRB 13

5. Fill in the missing numbers.

in	out
25	125
99	199
174	274
565	665

Rule +100

MRB 100–101

6. Draw a polygon with 4 sides.

Sample answer:

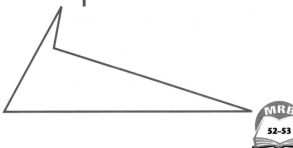

MRB 52–53

Date _____

1. Ask a partner to show times on a tool-kit clock.
   Draw the hands on the clock. Write the times to match.
   Answers vary.

____:____   ____:____   ____:____

2. Write a time for each clock face. Draw the hands to match.
   Answers vary.

____:____   ____:____   ____:____

3. Set your tool-kit clock to 3:00.
   How many minutes until 3:25? __25__ minutes

   Set your tool-kit clock to 1:30.
   How many minutes until 1:55? __25__ minutes

   Set your tool-kit clock to 10:45.
   How many minutes until 11:20? __35__ minutes

Math Boxes

1. Draw and solve.

There are 8 cups.

5 cups are dirty.

How many cups are clean?

___3___ cups

Sample drawing:

2. I buy a kite for $1.89.

I pay $2.00.

How much change do I get back?

___11___ ¢

3. Write <, >, or =.

305 ⟨<⟩ 385

113 ⟨=⟩ 100 + 13

129 ⟨<⟩

MRB
9–11

4. Complete the number-grid puzzle.

104	105		
	115		
	125		
134		136	

5. Write the number that is 10 more.

___89___   ___103___

MRB
10–11

6. Fill in the rule and the missing numbers.

Rule
+2

| 266 | 268 | 270 | 272 | 274 |

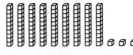

MRB
98–99

196 one hundred ninety-six

LESSON 10·3 Vending Machine Poster

LESSON 10·3 **Buying from the Vending Machine**

Pretend to buy items from the vending machine. Draw pictures or write the names of items you buy. Show the coins you use to pay for the items. Use Ⓝ, Ⓓ, and Ⓠ. Write the total cost.

1.

2.

Answers vary for Exercises 1–4.

3.

4.

Show the cost of these items. Use Ⓝ, Ⓓ, and Ⓠ.
Write the total cost. Sample answers:

5.

Ⓠ Ⓠ Ⓓ Ⓝ   Ⓓ Ⓓ Ⓓ Ⓓ Ⓝ

Total cost: $ 1.10

6.

Ⓠ Ⓓ Ⓝ   Ⓠ Ⓓ

Total cost: $ 0.75

Date

1. Record the times.

First-Grade Bedtimes

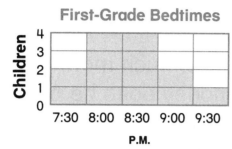

Earliest bedtime: 7:30

Latest bedtime: 9:30

Range: 2 hours

MRB
44–45

2. Clay has $1 Q D D D.

Rosa has Q Q Q Q Q Q.

Who has more money?

Rosa

How much more money?

20 ¢

3. Measure the line segment.

It is about ____ inches long.

Fill in the circle next to the best answer.

○ **A.** 9   ○ **B.** 3

● **C.** $3\frac{1}{2}$ ○ **D.** $8\frac{1}{2}$

MRB
65

4. Circle the bigger fraction.

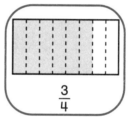

$\frac{3}{4}$

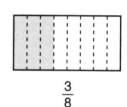

$\frac{3}{8}$

MRB
13

5. Fill in the missing numbers.

in

Rule

+10

out

in	out
8	18
76	86
93	103
254	264

MRB
100–101

6.

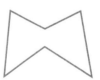

How many sides?

6 sides

How many corners?

6 corners

MRB
52–53

LESSON 10·4 **Math Boxes**

1. Draw and solve.

Amelia has 12 checkers.

6 checkers are black.

How many checkers are not black?

Sample drawing:

__6__ checkers

2. A magnet costs $1.39.

Jamal has $1.25.

How much more money does he need?

___14___ ¢

$1.39

3. Write <, >, or =.

 = $1.25

Q D D N D > $0.50

Q Q Q D D D > $1.00

MRB 9, 88, 89

4. Complete the number-grid puzzle.

302	303	304
	313	314
	323	
332		334

5. Write the number that is 10 more.

 145

218

MRB 10–11

6. Fill in the rule and the missing numbers.

Rule **+10**

| 128 | 138 | 148 | 158 | 168 |

MRB 98–99

Date _____

Triangles

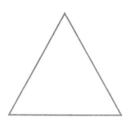 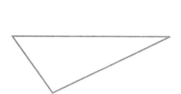 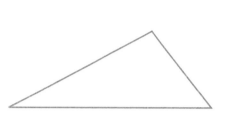

Quadrangles (Quadrilaterals)

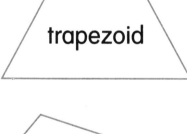
trapezoid

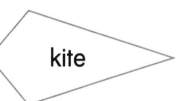
kite

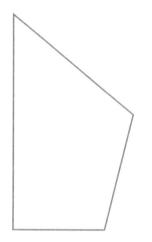

rhombus

square

rectangle

Other Polygons

hexagon

octagon

pentagon

heptagon

Date _____

Use straws and twist-ties to make the following polygons.
Draw the polygons. Record the number of corners and sides
for each polygon.

Sample drawings are given for Exercises 1–3.

1. Make a square.

   Number of sides ___4___

   Number of corners ___4___

2. Make a triangle.

   Number of sides ___3___

   Number of corners ___3___

3. Make a hexagon.

   Number of sides ___6___

   Number of corners ___6___

4. Make a polygon of your choice. Answers vary.

   Write its name. _____

   Number of sides _____

   Number of corners _____

5. Make another polygon of your choice. Answers vary.

   Write its name. _____

   Number of sides _____

   Number of corners _____

LESSON 10·5 **Reviewing 3-Dimensional Shapes**

Word Bank

sphere	rectangular prism	pyramid
cube	cone	cylinder

Write the name of each 3-dimensional shape.

1.

_____cone_____

2.

_____cube_____

3.

rectangular prism

4.

_____sphere_____

5.

_____pyramid_____

6.

_____cylinder_____

Five Regular Polyhedrons

The faces that make each shape are identical.

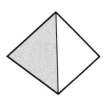 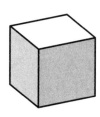  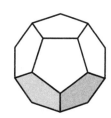 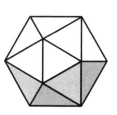

tetrahedron	cube	octahedron	dodecahedron	icosahedron
4 faces	6 faces	8 faces	12 faces	20 faces

LESSON 10·5 Math Boxes

1. Solve.

$\frac{1}{2}$ of 50¢ = ____25____ ¢

$\frac{1}{2}$ of \$1.00 = ____50____ ¢

$\frac{1}{2}$ of \$2.00 = \$__1__.__00__

2. Which are you more likely to grab?

black or white? __white__

○ or □? ____○____

47–48

3. Record the time.

____5____ : ____15____

80–81

4. Shade the thermometer to show 78° F.

87

5. Label each part.

Shade $\frac{2}{6}$ of the hexagon.

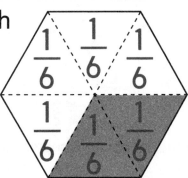

Write another name for $\frac{2}{6}$.

$\frac{1}{3}$
____

13

6. These are pictures of 3-dimensional shapes. Put an X on shapes that have all flat faces.

pyramid   sphere   cylinder   cube

58

LESSON 10·6

U.S. Weather Map

U.S. Weather Map: Spring High/Low Temperatures (°F)

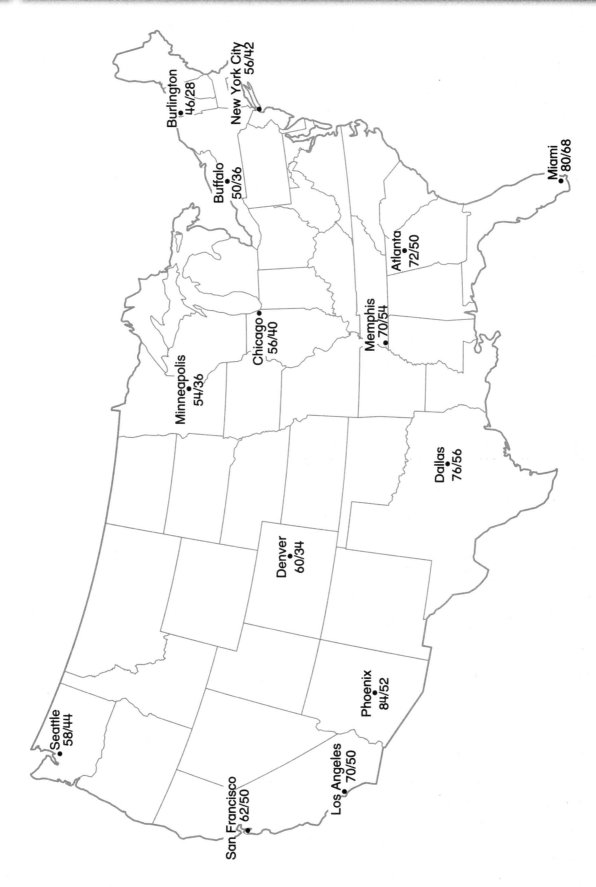

Burlington 46/28

New York City 56/42

Buffalo 50/36

Miami 80/68

Atlanta 72/50

Chicago 56/40

Memphis 70/54

Minneapolis 54/36

Dallas 76/56

Denver 60/34

Phoenix 84/52

Seattle 58/44

Los Angeles 70/50

San Francisco 62/50

Date _____

1.

City	Warmest Temperature	Coldest Temperature	Difference
Answers vary.	_____ °F	_____ °F	_____ °F
_____	_____ °F	_____ °F	_____ °F
_____	_____ °F	_____ °F	_____ °F

2. Of your 3 cities, Answers vary.

_____ has the warmest temperature at _____ °F.

_____ has the coldest temperature at _____ °F.

The difference between these two temperatures is _____ °F.

---

3. On the map,

___Phoenix___ has the warmest temperature at _84_ °F.

___Burlington___ has the coldest temperature at _28_ °F.

The difference between these two temperatures is _56_ °F.

LESSON 10·6

Math Boxes

1. Draw and solve.

Mateo wants to read 8 books.

He has read 2 books.

How many more books does Mateo have to read?

___6___ books

Sample drawing:

2. Sunglasses cost $3.99.

I pay $5.00.

How much change do I get back?

Fill in the circle next to the best answer.

○ **A.** $2.99   ○ **B.** $8.99

○ **C.** $8.00   ● **D.** $1.01

3. Write <, >, or =.

10 + 23 $<$ 40

18 + 5 $=$ 5 + 18

32 $>$ 51 − 20

Half of 50 $=$ 25

MRB 9

4. Complete the puzzle.

168		170
	179	
	189	
198		200

5. Write the number that is 10 less.

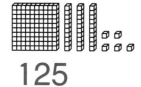

___125___

___198___

MRB 10–11

6. Fill in the missing numbers.

Rule
+100

 84   184   284   384   484

MRB 98–99

LESSON 10·7 **Math Boxes**

---

1. $2.00 =

___200___ pennies

___40___ nickels

___20___ dimes

___8___ quarters

MRB 88–89

---

2. Which are you more likely to grab?

black or white? ___black___

○ or □? ___○___

MRB 47–48

---

3. Draw the hands to show 10:45.

MRB 80–81

---

4. What is the temperature? Fill in the circle next to the best answer.

● **A.** 82°F

○ **B.** 85°F

○ **C.** 80°F

○ **D.** 90°F

90— °F
80—
70—
60—
50—

MRB 87

---

5. Divide the square into $\frac{1}{4}$s.

Shade $\frac{2}{4}$.

Sample answer:

Write another name for $\frac{2}{4}$.

___$\frac{1}{2}$___

MRB 13

---

6. These are pictures of 3-dimensional shapes. Put an X on shapes with curved faces.

cone   sphere   prism   pyramid

MRB 58

Date

1. What time is it?

<u> 6 </u> : <u> 40 </u>

MRB
80–81

2. Write the amount.

Ⓠ Ⓝ Ⓓ Ⓟ Ⓟ Ⓓ

<u> 52 </u> ¢

3. What day is it today?

<u>Answers vary.</u>

What day will it be tomorrow?

<u>Answers vary.</u>

4. Complete the number-grid puzzle.

	125	
134	135	136
144	145	146

5. Count by 2s.

36, <u>38</u>, <u>40</u>,

42, <u>44</u>, <u>46</u>,

48, <u>50</u>, <u>52</u>,

<u>54</u>, 56, <u>58</u>

6. What is the temperature?

<u> 62 </u> °F

°F

90 —
80 —
70 —
60 —
50 —

MRB
87

Date _____ Time _____

Notes

Date _____ Time _____

Notes

Date _____ Time _____

Notes